Bastien Music Flashcards

In addition to the written activities in this book, the use of flashcards is highly recommended to aid in recognizing individual notes. *Music Flashcards* (GP27) by Jane Smisor Bastien may be obtained from your local music dealer. Each flashcard is numbered. As new notes are introduced throughout the book, they will be pictured at the bottom of the page. Each card will have a number on it in the picture. Find the numbered cards from your set of music flashcards then name, play, and memorize these new notes.

New Notes: This icon is used whenever any new notes are presented.

LINE NOTES AND SPACE NOTES

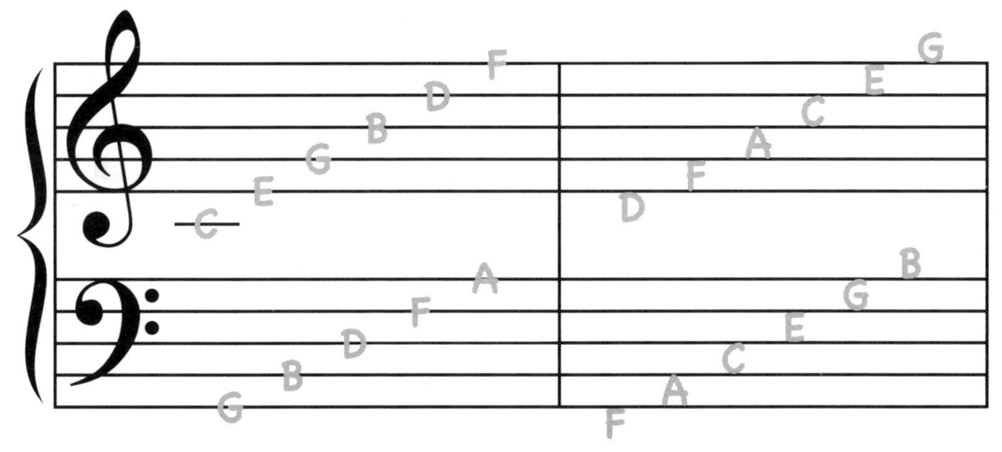

Name each interval: step up, step down, skip up, skip down or same (repeated note).

Draw each skip, step, or repeated note.

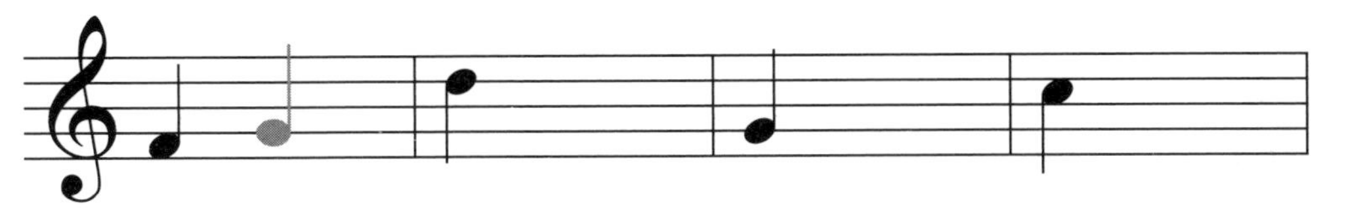

1. step up 2. skip down 3. repeat 4. step down

5. skip up 6. repeat 7. step down 8. skip down

Line Notes

A. Write the letter names of the keys in the blanks to form skips up the keyboard.

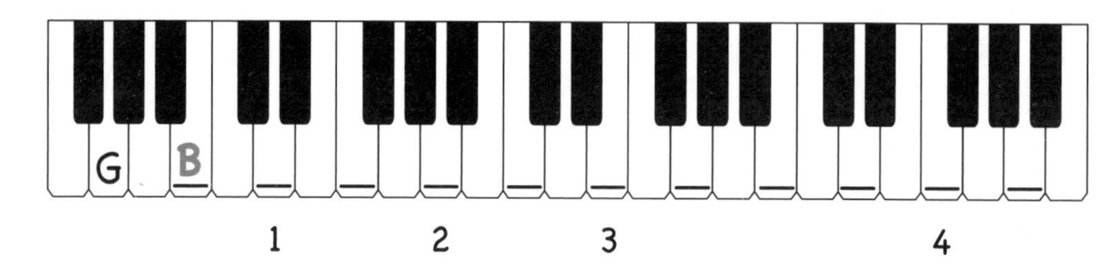

B. Fill in the blanks with letters from above to complete the riddle.

Q: Wh__e__r_____ _____o _____ish
3 3 1 4

k _____ _____p th _____ir mon_____y?
3 3 3 3

A: In _____ riv_____r b_____nk!
2 3 2

A. Write the note name inside each note.

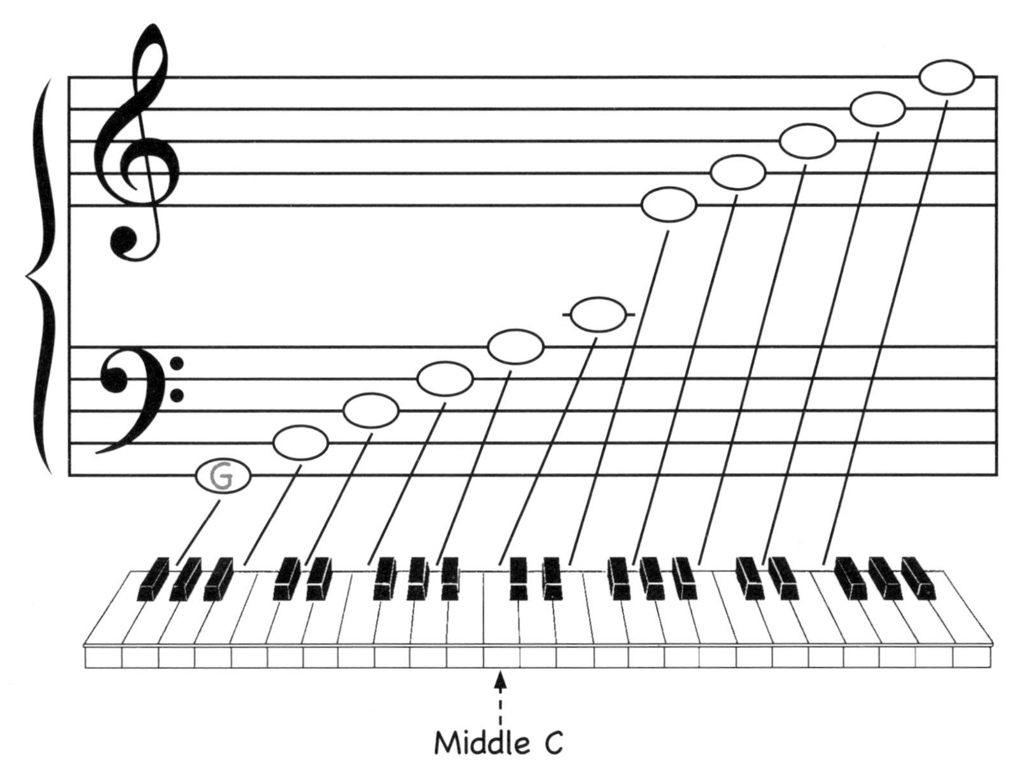

B. Fill in each blank with the correct note name.

C. Unscramble the letters in the circles to answer the riddle.

1. **F** up a skip __A__ up a skip _____ down a step? (_____)

2. **D** down a skip _____ up a step _____ down a skip? (_____)

3. **G** up a skip _____ up a skip _____ down a step? (_____)

Q: How do you get from the Bronx to Manhattan?

A: _____ _____ _____

A. Write the letter names of the lines notes three times.

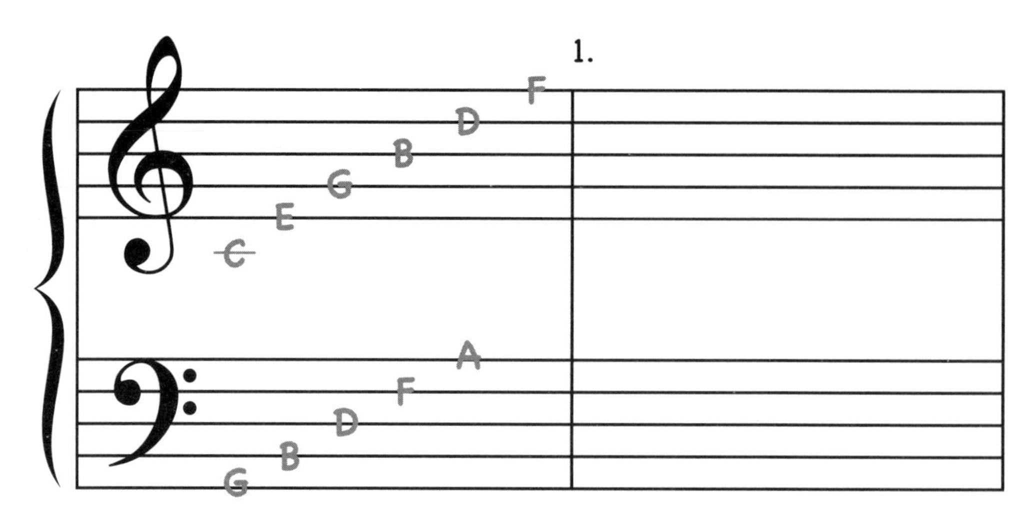

B. Unscramble the letters to solve the riddles:

Q: What is full of holes but still holds water?

A: A ___ ___ ___ ___ ___ ___

G N S O P E

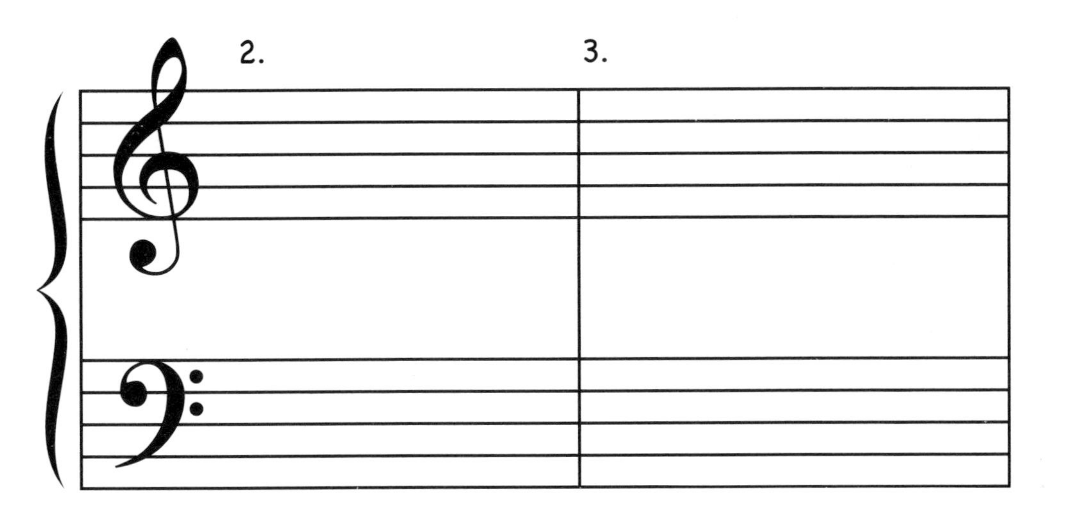

Q: What flies without wings?

A: ____ ____ ____ ____

M T E I

A. Name each note.

B. Write the numbered notes on the staff in the correct place on the keyboard.

1. B   2. ___   3. ___   4. ___   5. ___   6. ___

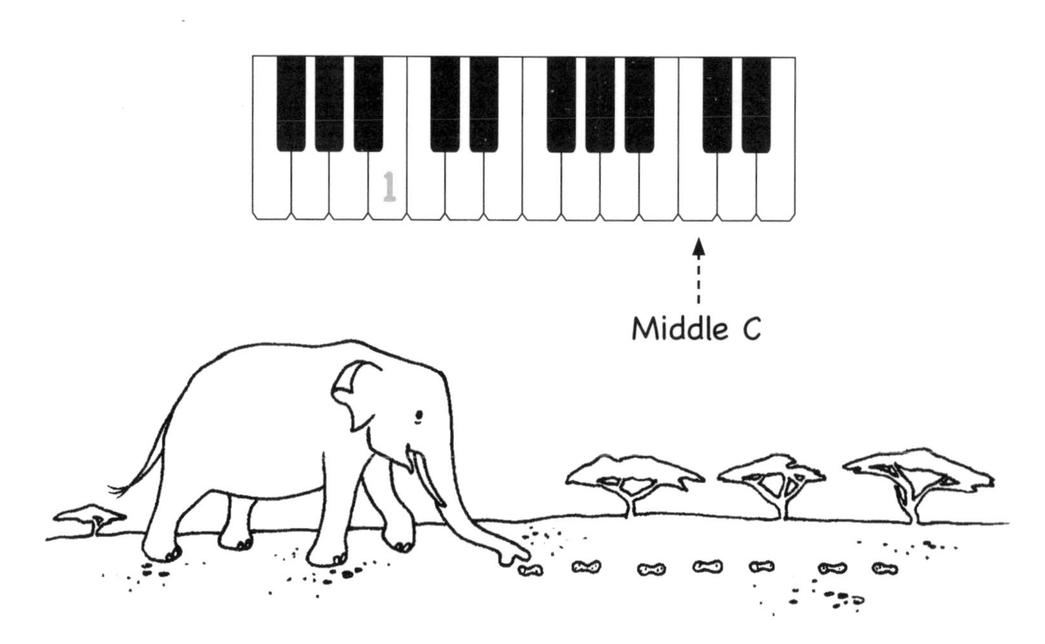

NEW NOTES!

Bastien Music Flashcards GP27: Practice naming and playing the 𝄢 line notes until you can recognize them easily.

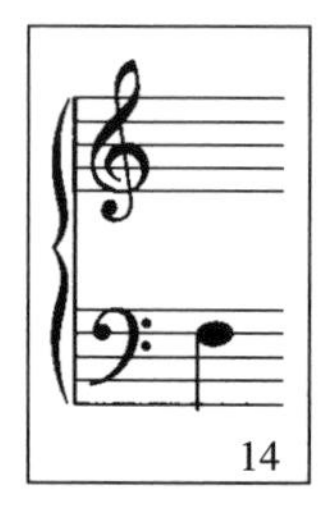

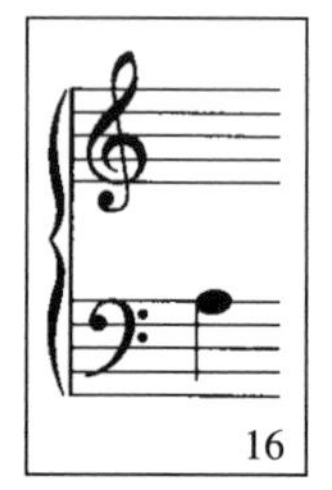

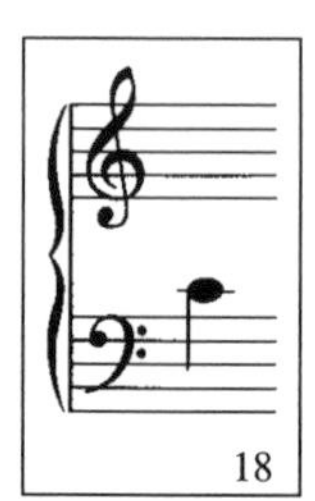

A. Name each note.
B. Write the numbered notes on the staff in the correct place on the keyboard.

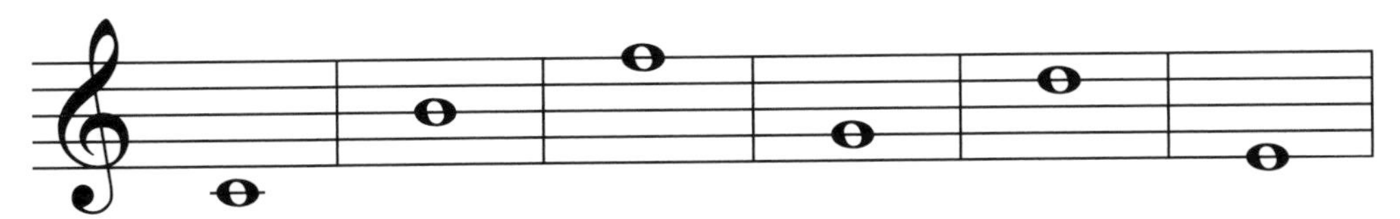

1. C   2.___   3.___   4.___   5.___   6.___

NEW NOTES!

Bastien Music Flashcards GP27: Practice naming and playing the 𝄞 line notes until you can recognize them easily.

A. Draw each ***line note*** on the staff.
B. Write the numbered notes on the staff
   in the correct place on the keyboards.

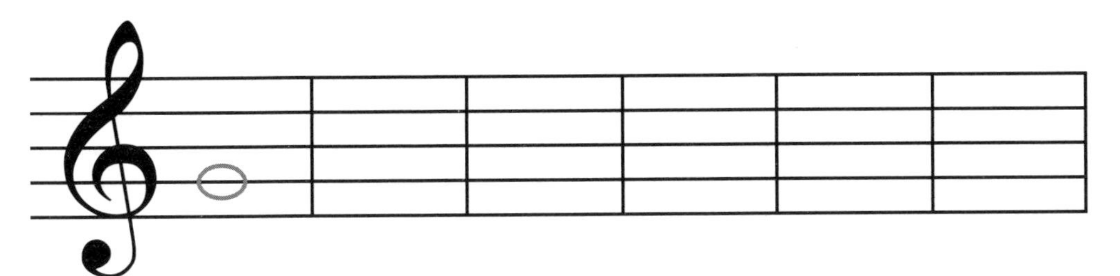

7. G   8. D   9. Middle C   10. E   11. B   12. F

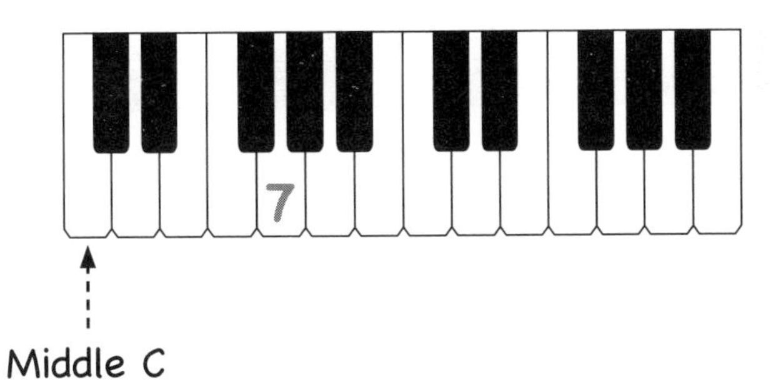

C. Fill in the blanks with note names from these pages to form a fun fact.

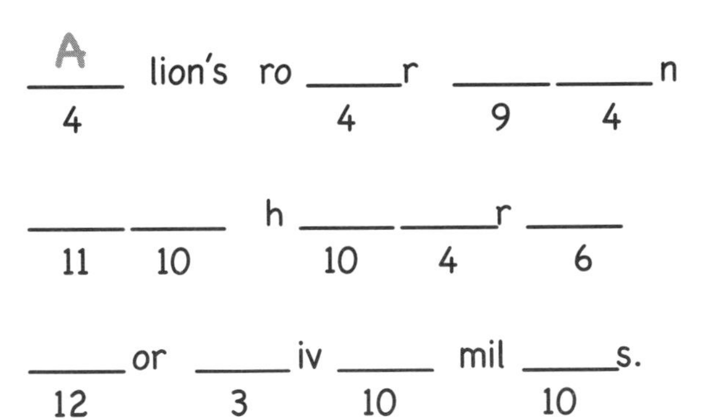

A. Name each note.

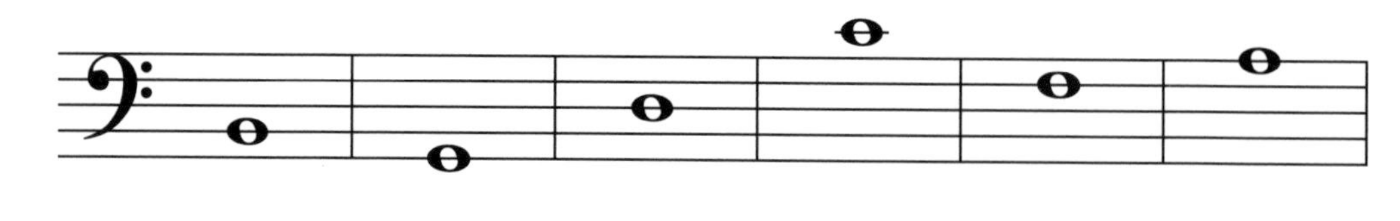

1.____ 2.____ 3.____ 4.____ 5.____ 6.____

B. Color the:

F's purple.
A's red.
C's orange.
B's blue.
D's green.
G's yellow.

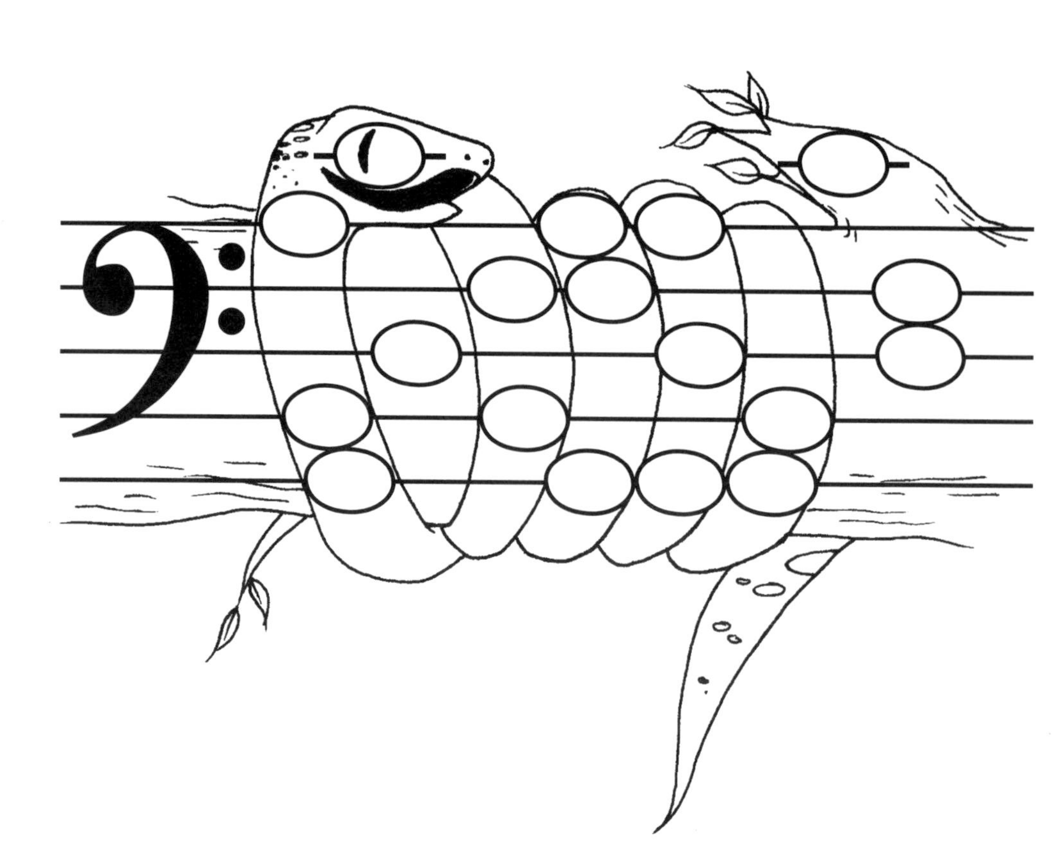

A. Name each note.

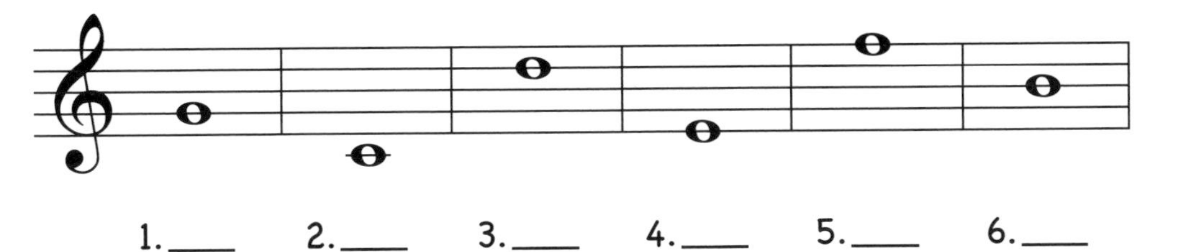

1.____ 2.____ 3.____ 4.____ 5.____ 6.____

B. Color the:

G's red.
F's orange.
D's yellow.
B's purple.
C's brown.
E's green

Space Notes

A. Write the letter names of the keys in the blanks to form skips up the keyboard.

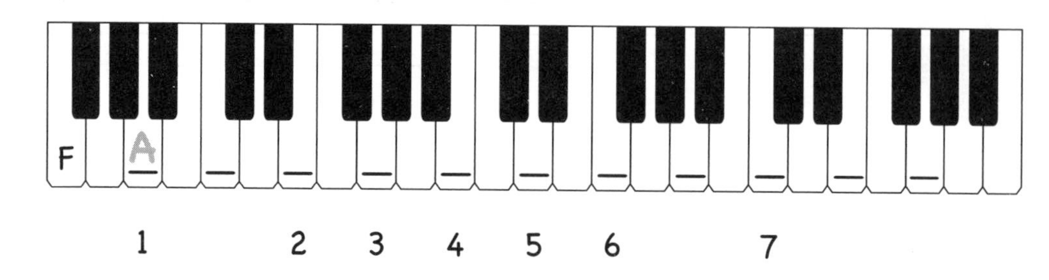

B. Fill in the blanks with note names from above to complete the riddle.

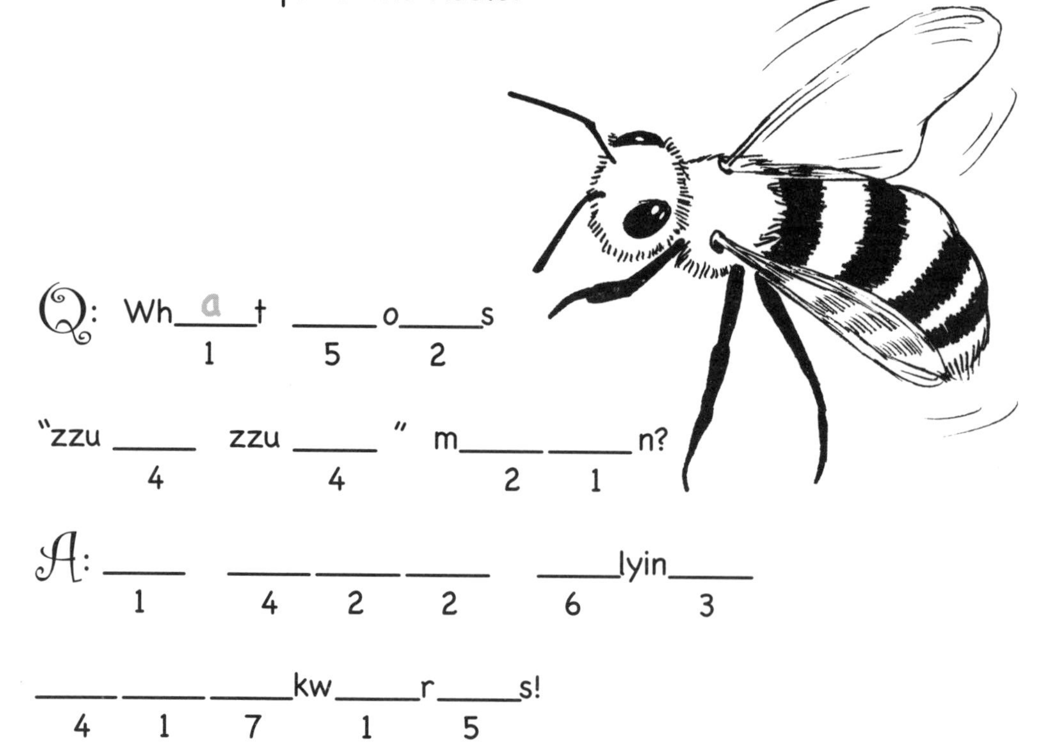

Q: Wh__a__t ____o____s
(1) (5) (2)

"zzu ____ zzu ____" m____ ____n?
(4) (4) (2) (1)

A: ____ ____ ____ ____ ____lyin____
(1) (4) (2) (2) (6) (3)

____ ____ ____kw____r____s!
(4) (1) (7) (1) (5)

A. Write the note name inside each note.

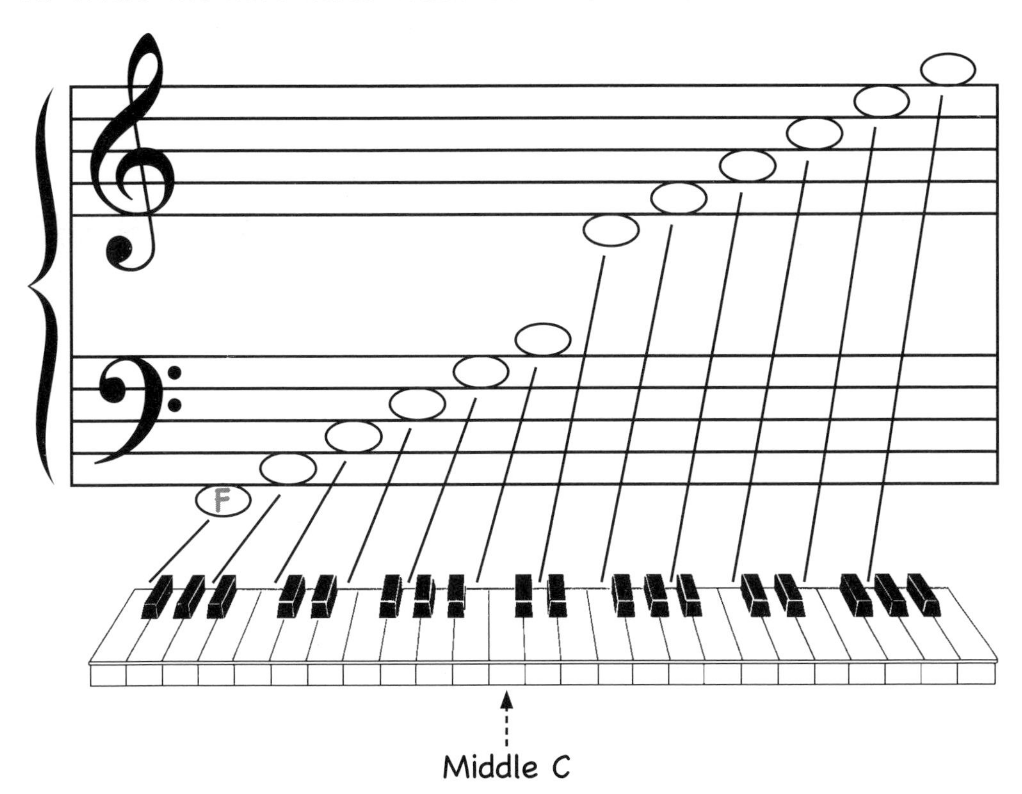

B. Fill in each blank with the correct note name.
Unscramble the letters in the circles to answer the riddle.

1. **E** up a skip __G__ up a skip _____ down a step? _____

2. **C** up a skip ____ up a step _____ down a skip? _____

3. **G** down a skip _____ up a step _____ down a skip? _____

Q: When Mom says, "No!" Who should you ask?

A: ____ ____ ____

A. Write the letter names of the space notes three times:

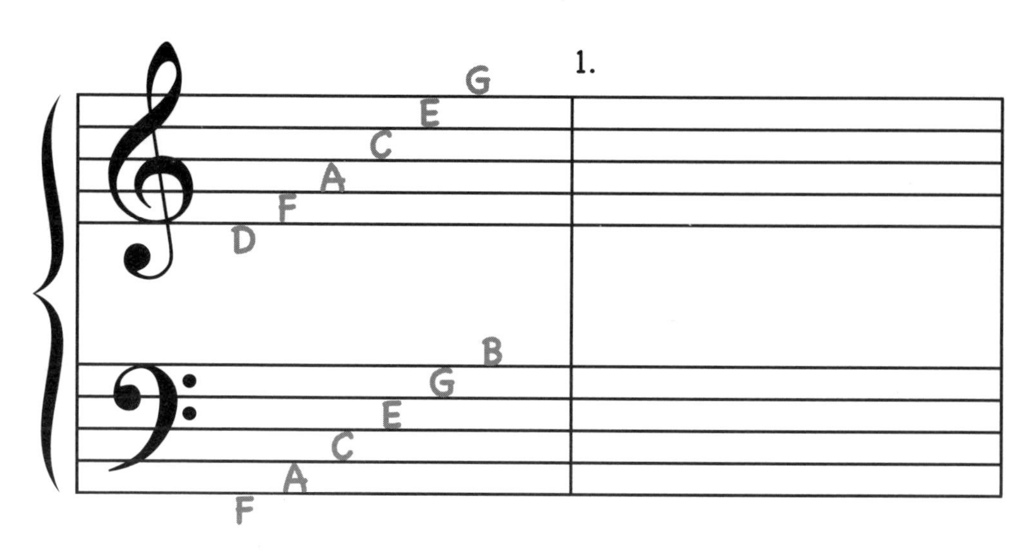

B. Unscramble the letters to solve the riddle.

Q: What is black and white and "red" all over?

A: A ____ ____ ____ ____ ____ ____ ____ ____ ____

W N E P R S P A E

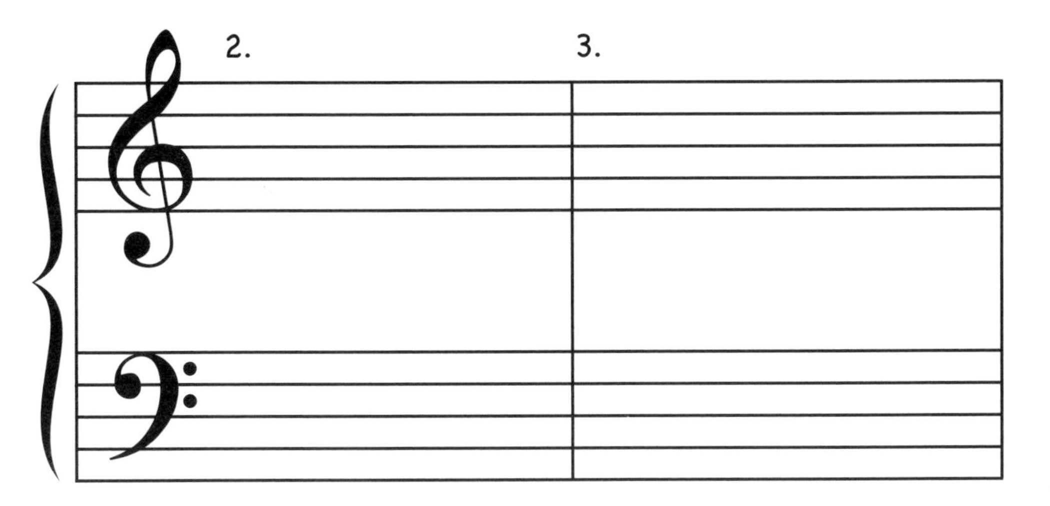
2.
3.

A. Name each note.

B. Write the numbered notes on the staff in the correct place on the keyboard.

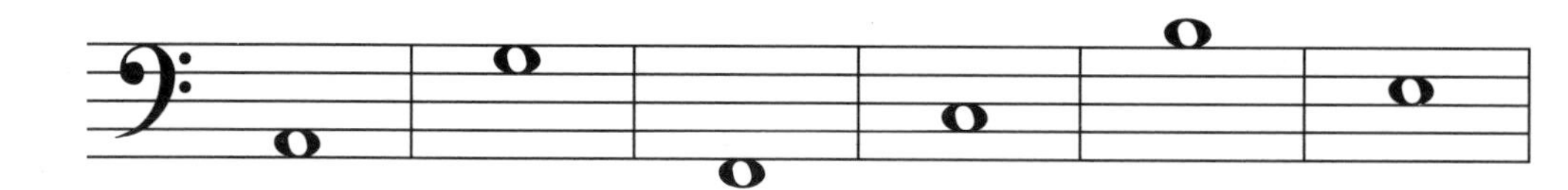

1. A___ 2. ____ 3. ____ 4. ____ 5. ____ 6. ____

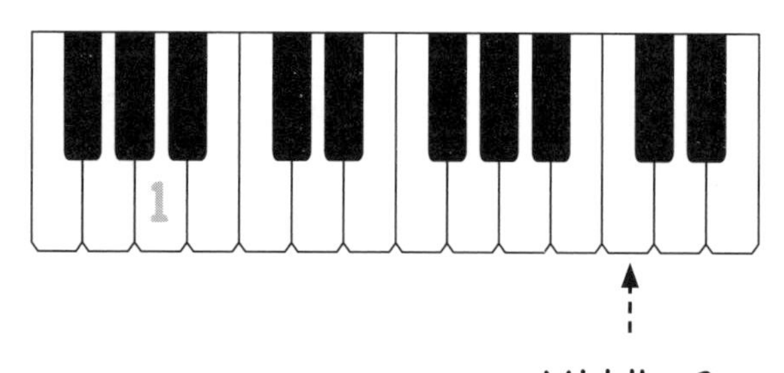

NEW NOTES!

Bastien Music Flashcards GP27: Practice naming and playing the 𝄢 line notes until you can recognize them easily.

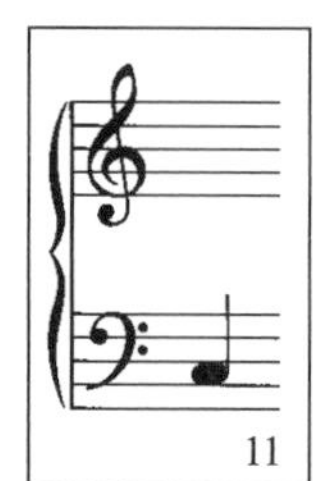

A. Name each note.

B. Write the numbered notes on the staff in the correct place on the keyboard.

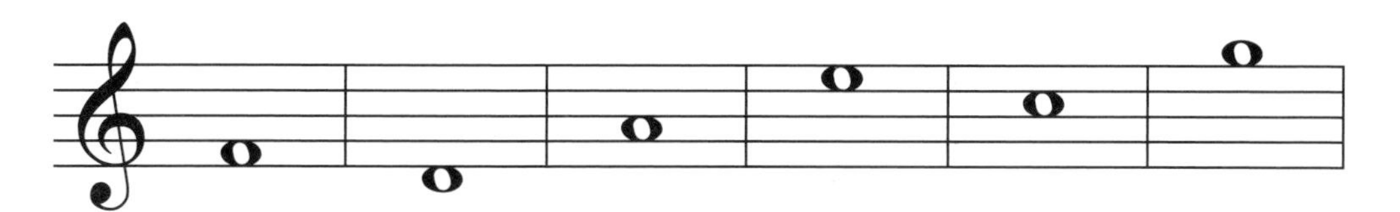

1. F 2. ____ 3. ____ 4. ____ 5. ____ 6. ____

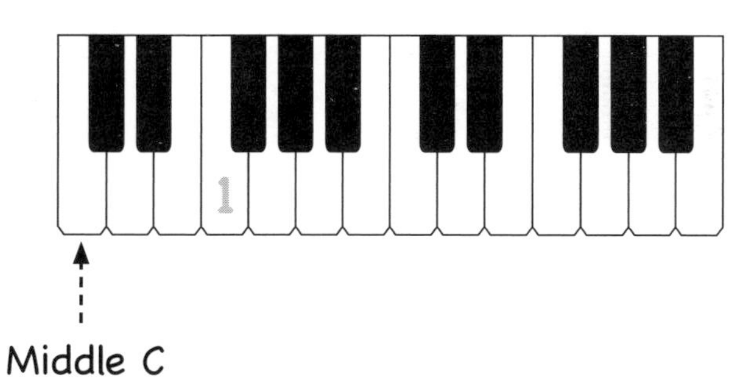

NEW NOTES!

Bastien Music Flashcards GP27: Practice naming and playing the 𝄞 line notes until you can recognize them easily.

A. Draw each ***space note*** on the staff.

B. Write the numbered notes on the staff in the correct place on the keyboard.

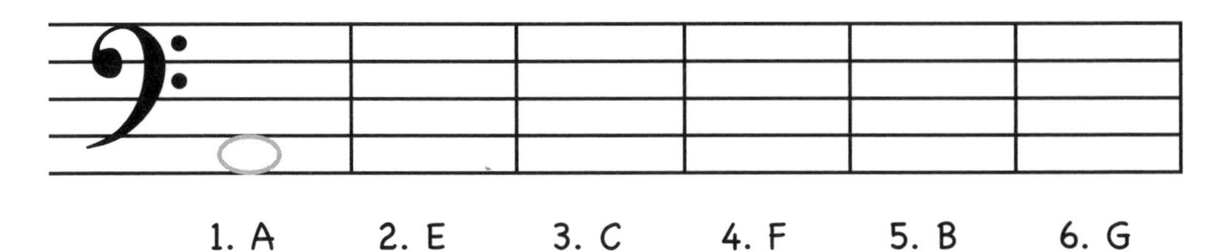

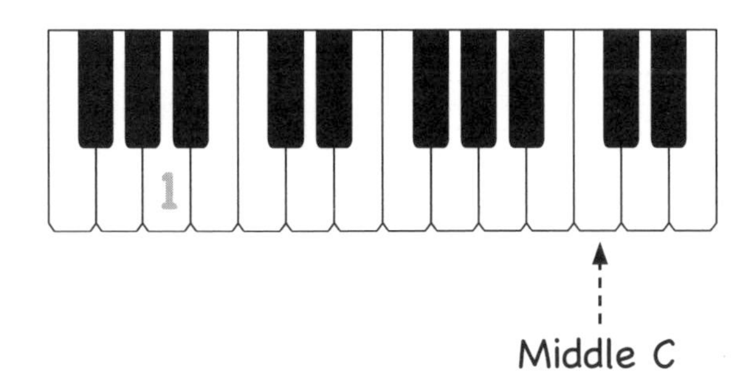

C. Fill in the blanks with note names from above to form a fun fact.

Q: Are zebras' stripes black over white or white over black?

A: E___ ___ ___h z___ ___r___ h___s its own
2 1 3 2 5 1 1

uniqu___ p___tt___rn o___
2 1 2 4

whit___ strip___s on ___l___ck.
2 2 5 1

A. Draw each ***space note*** on the staff.
B. Write the numbered notes on the staff in the correct place on the keyboard.

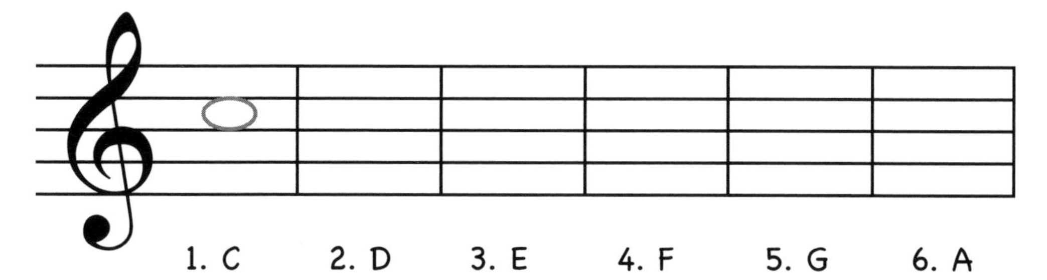

A. Name each note.

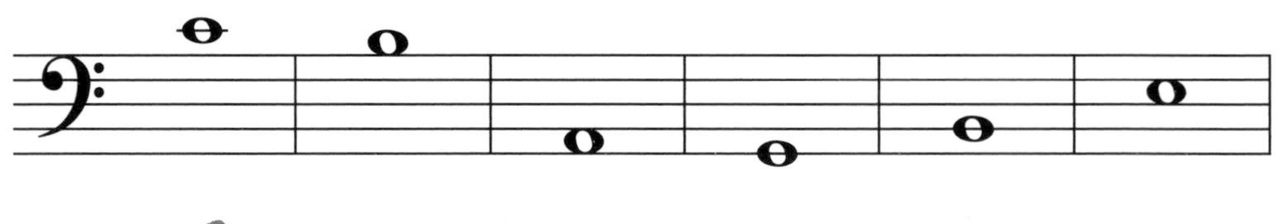

1. C   2. ____   3. ____   4. ____   5. ____   6. ____

7. ____   8. ____   9. ____   10. ____   11. ____   12. ____

B. Fill in the blanks with note names from above to form a fun fact.

Hippopot__a__mus____s liv____ in w____t____r
(3, 6, 6, 11, 6)

____ut ____ ____nnot swim!
(2, 1, 11)

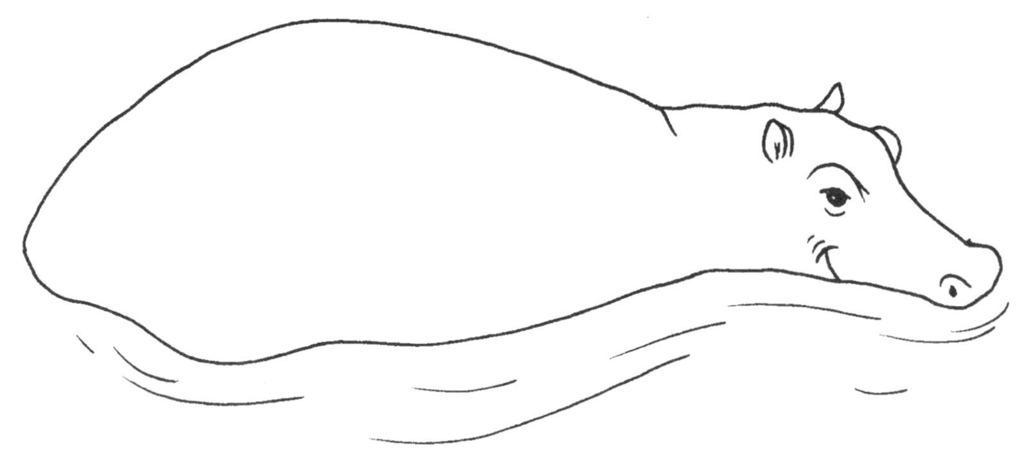

Name the notes to form words.

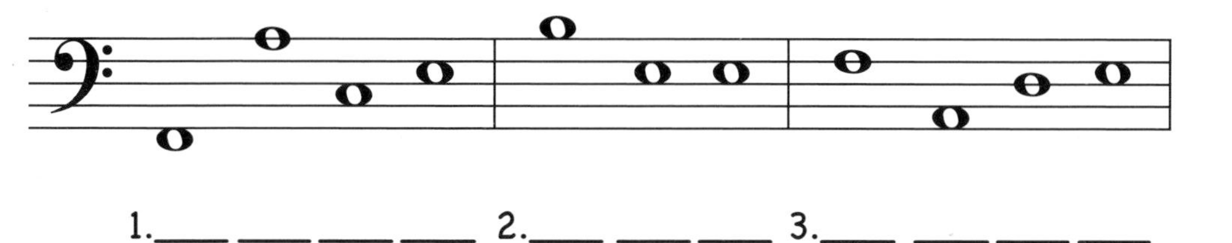

1.____ ____ ____ ____ 2.____ ____ ____ 3.____ ____ ____ ____

4.____ ____ ____ ____ ____ ____ ____ 5.____ ____ ____ ____

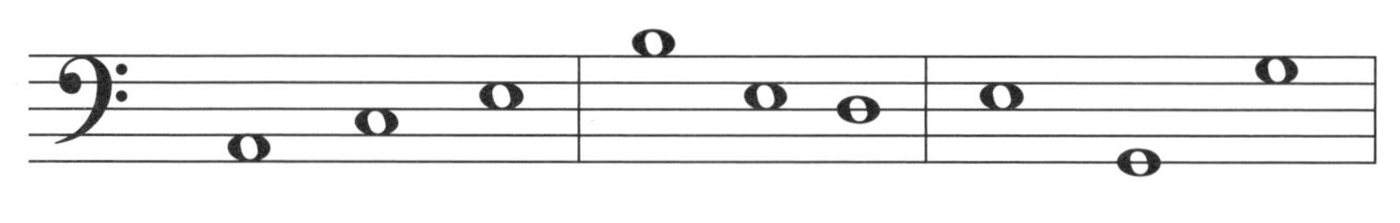

6.____ ____ ____ 7.____ ____ ____ 8.____ ____ ____

Name the given note, then draw and name the second note as directed.

Name the notes to form words.

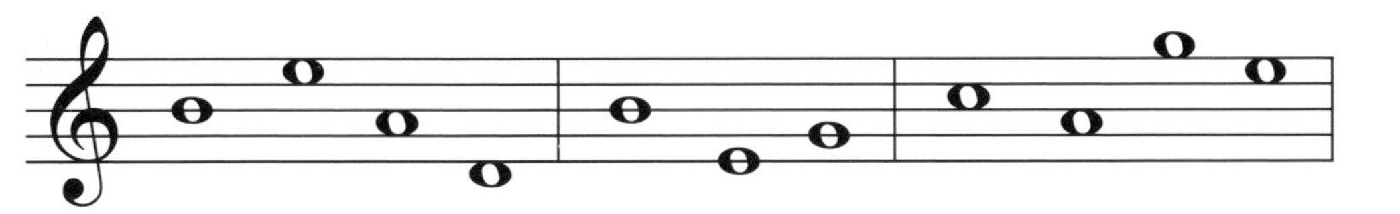

1. ___ ___ ___ ___ 2. ___ ___ ___ 3. ___ ___ ___ ___

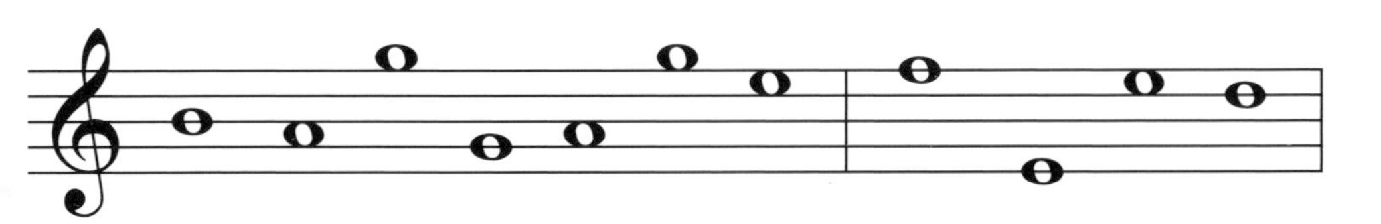

4. ___ ___ ___ ___ ___ ___ ___ 5. ___ ___ ___ ___

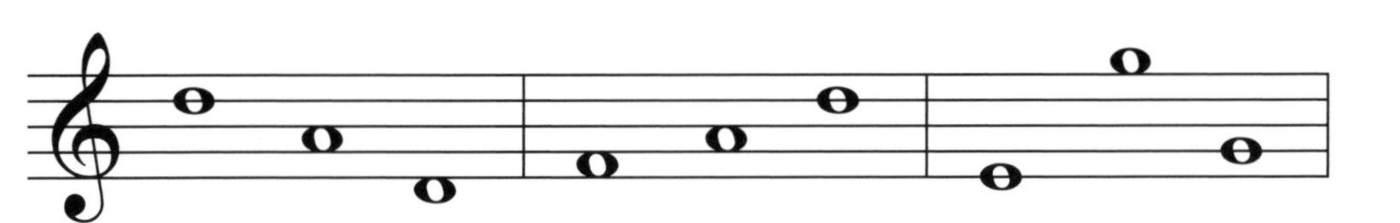

6. ___ ___ ___ 7. ___ ___ ___ 8. ___ ___ ___

Color the:

C's red. D's brown.
E's green. A's black.
B's purple. F's yellow.
G's orange.

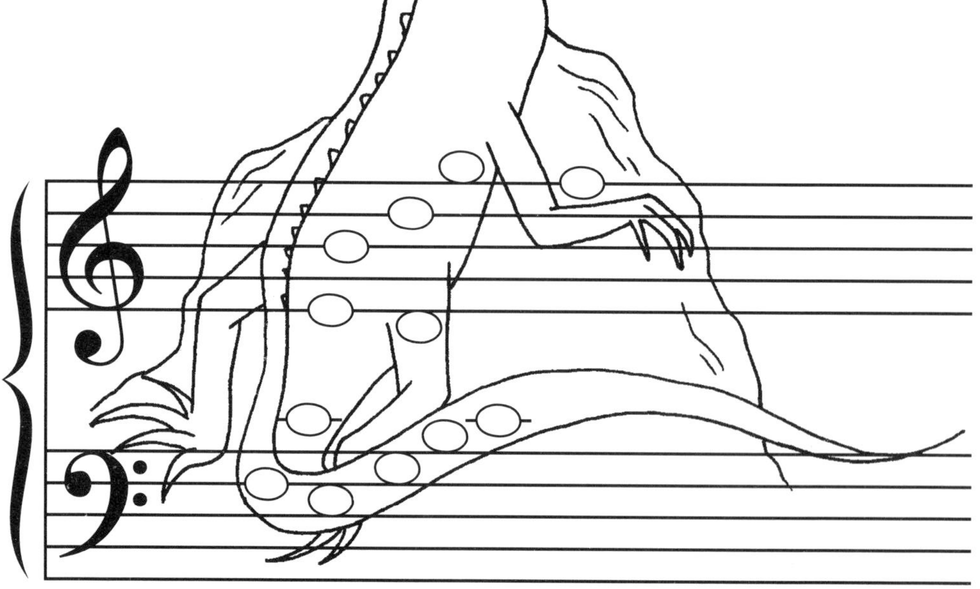

Who Am I?

1. I am the space below the 𝄢. Who am I? F
2. I am the 2nd space of the 𝄞. Who am I? _____
3. I am the space above the 𝄞. Who am I? _____
4. I am the 3rd space of the 𝄢. Who am I? _____
5. I am the 4th line of the 𝄞. Who am I? _____
6. I am the space below the 𝄞. Who am I? _____
7. I am the 1st line of the 𝄢. Who am I? _____
8. I am the 4th space of the 𝄞. Who am I? _____
9. I am the 2nd space of the 𝄢. Who am I? _____
10. I am the 3rd line of the 𝄞. Who am I? _____

Dot to Dot

A. Write the note name inside each note.
B. Follow the numbers and connect the dots.

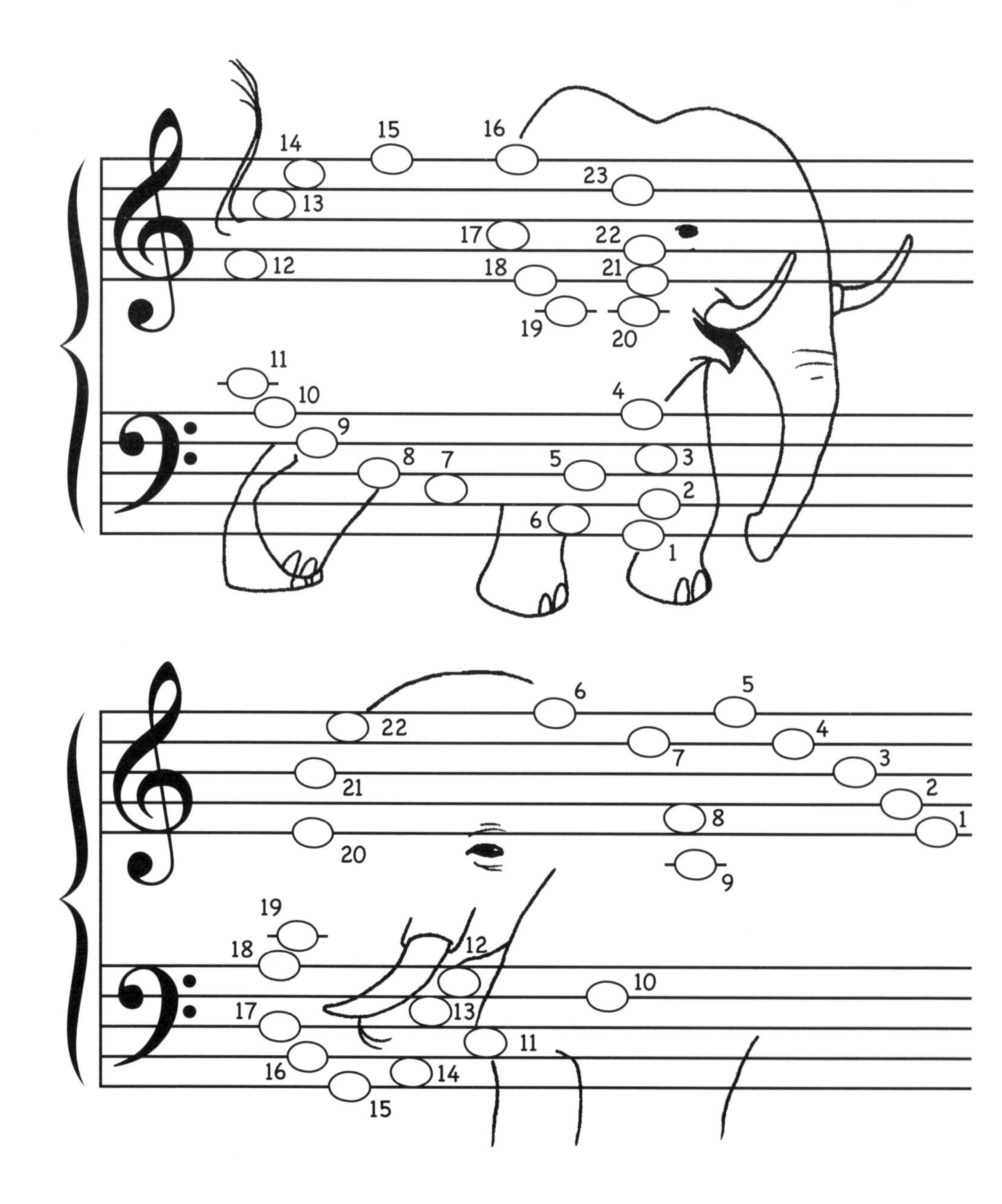

Write the numbered notes on the staff in the correct place on the keyboard.

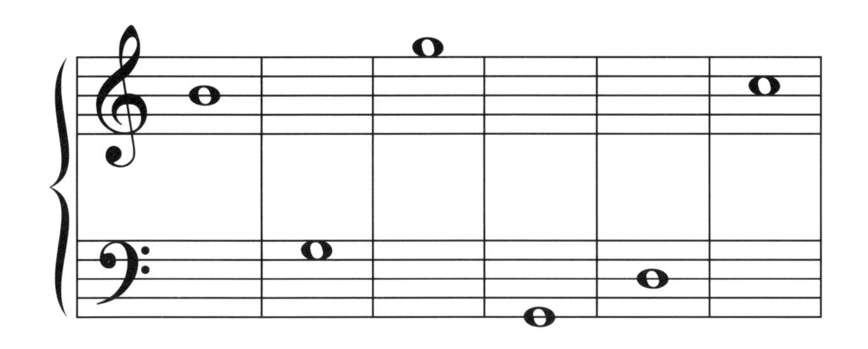

1. B 2.____ 3.____ 4.____ 5.____ 6.____

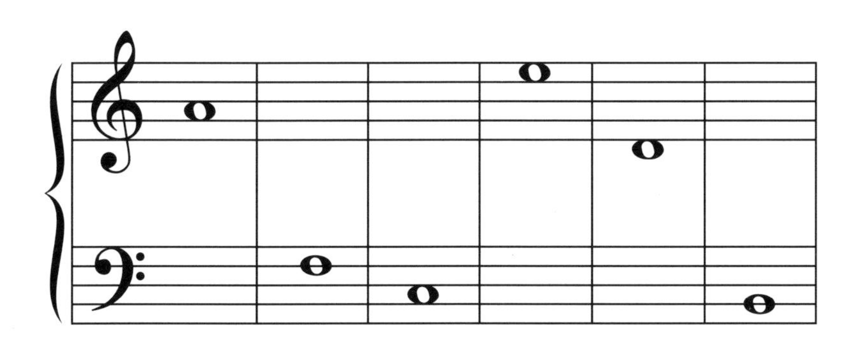

7.____ 8.____ 9.____ 10.____ 11.____ 12.____

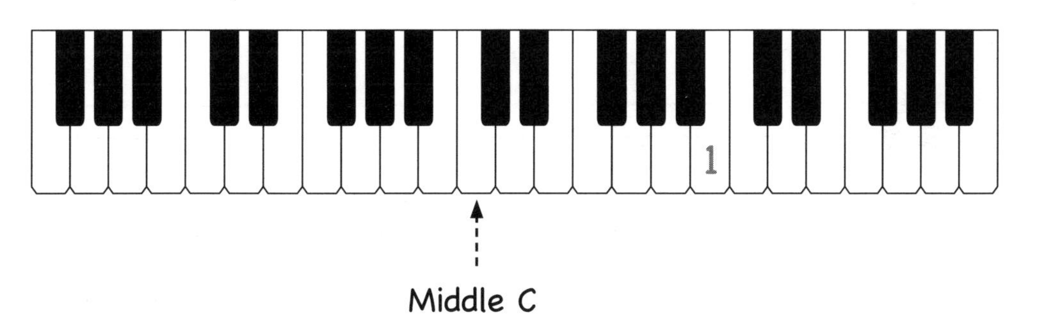

Who Am I?

1. I am the 4th space of the 𝄢 . Who am I? G
2. I am the space above the 𝄢. Who am I? _____
3. I am the 2nd line of the 𝄞. Who am I? _____
4. I am the 3rd space of the 𝄢 . Who am I? _____
5. I am the line between 𝄞 and 𝄢 . Who am I? _____
6. I am the 3rd line of the 𝄢 . Who am I? _____
7. I am the 1st space of the 𝄞 . Who am I? _____
8. I am the 1st space of the 𝄢 . Who am I? _____
9. I am the 1st line of the 𝄞 . Who am I? _____
10. I am the 2nd line of the 𝄢 . Who am I? _____

Color the:

C's red.
E's blue.
G's yellow.
B's orange.
F's purple.
A's brown.
D's green.

____

can name all of the line notes and space notes on the staff with ease!

____

Teacher's Signature